Little Vo
The Beach

Published by
Novello Publishing Limited
14-15 Berners Street, London, W1T 3LJ, UK.

Exclusive distributors:
Music Sales Limited
Distribution Centre, Newmarket Road,
Bury St Edmunds, Suffolk IP33 3YB, UK.

Music Sales Pty Limited
Units 3-4, 17 Willfox Street, Condell Park, NSW 2200, Australia.

Order No. NOV163625   ISBN 978-1-78305-104-5
This book © Copyright 2013 Novello & Company Limited.

Arranged by Jonathan Wikeley.
Music processed by Paul Ewers Music Design.
Edited by Ruth Power.
Piano by Paul Knight.
Singers: Rachel Lindley, Sinead O'Kelly, Lucy Potterton.
Engineered, mixed & mastered by Jonas Persson.

Printed in the EU.

www.musicsales.com

NOVELLO PUBLISHING LIMITED
part of The Music Sales Group
London / New York / Paris / Sydney / Copenhagen / Berlin / Madrid / Hong Kong / Tokyo

Don't Worry Baby

Words & Music by Brian Wilson & Roger Christian

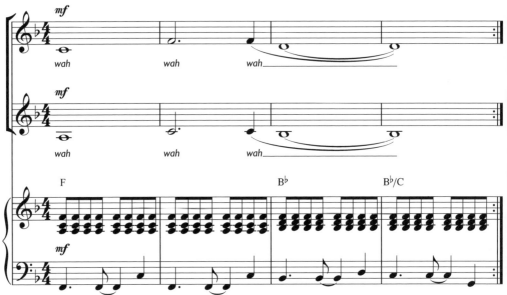

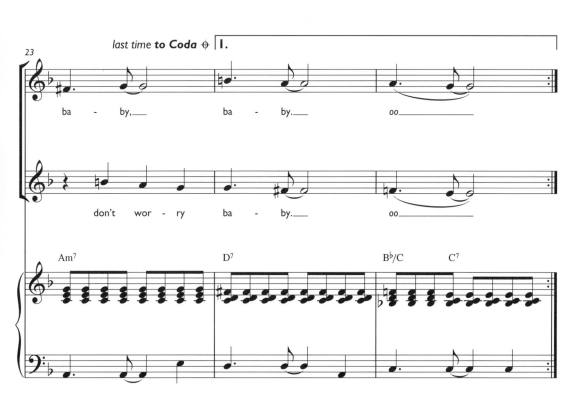

ba - by.___ oo_____ bap bap

ba - by.___ oo_____ bap bap

D⁷   B♭/C   C⁷   F

bap bap   bap bap   bap bap   bap bap

bap bap   bap bap   bap bap   bap bap

B♭   B♭/C   F

bap   bap   bap   bap   bap   bap

bap   bap   bap   bap   bap   bap

B♭   B♭/C

Coda

mp

ba - - by,_____   yeah.

mp

ba - - by,_____   yeah.

D⁷   G

mp

God Only Knows

Words & Music by Brian Wilson & Tony Asher

last time **to Coda** ⊕

1.

___ what I'd be with - out you.
___ what I'd be with - out you.

___ what I'd be with - out you.
___ what I'd be with - out you.

C/E

Dm7

C

2.

F/C

E♭

F/C

mf

ba ba ba___ ba ba   ba   ba ba   ba ba___

ba ba ba___ ba ba   ba   ba ba   ba ba___

D.S. al Coda

God on - ly knows___ what I'd   be   with - out___   you.

ah___

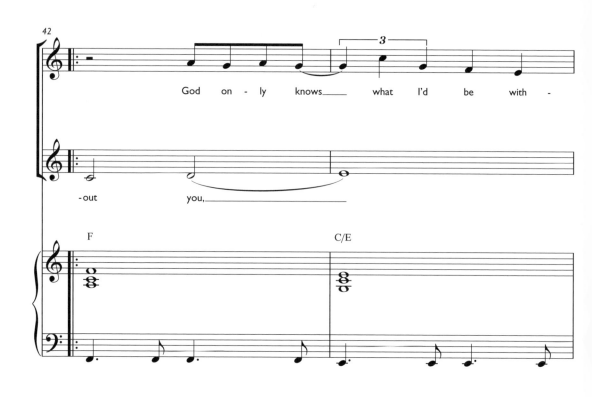

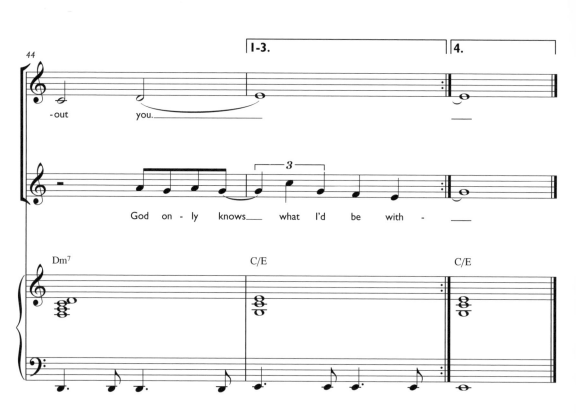

Good Vibrations

Words & Music by Brian Wilson & Mike Love

16

19

Got - ta keep___ those lov - in' good vi - bra - tions a - hap - 'nin' with her.

Got - ta keep___ those lov - in' good vi - bra - tions a - hap - 'nin' with her.

Got - ta keep___ those lov - in' good vi - bra - tions a - hap - 'nin' with her.

Got - ta keep___ those lov - in' good vi - bra - tions a - hap - 'nin' with her.

Got - ta keep___ those lov - in' good... *ah*___

Got - ta keep___ those lov - in' good... *ah*___

Good, good, good, *oo bap bap,* good vi... bra-tions.

Good, good good, good vi - bra-tions, *bap bap,* good vi... bra-tions.

play 3 times

In My Room

Words & Music by Brian Wilson & Gary Usher

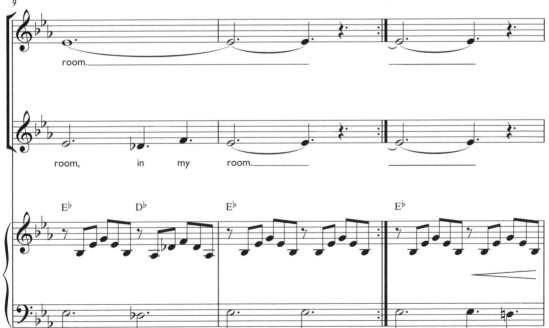

and my sigh - ing, laugh at yes - ter - day.

and my sigh - ing, laugh at yes - ter - day.

B♭　　　　　Fm⁷　　　　A♭/B♭　　B♭

mp

Coda

room, in my room.

E♭　　　D♭　　　E♭

Wouldn't It Be Nice

Words & Music by Brian Wilson, Tony Asher & Mike Love

Would-n't it be nice if we were old - er, then we would-n't
nice if we would wake___ up in the morn - ing

Would-n't it be nice if we were old - er, then we would-n't
nice if we would wake___ up in the morn - ing

have to wait__ so long,_____ and would - n't it be nice to live to - geth-
when the day__ is new,_____ and af - ter hav - ing spent the day to - geth-

$D^\flat$ $B^\flat m^7$ $E^{\flat 7}$ $A^\flat$

- er in the kind of world where we____ be - long?_____
- er, hold each oth - er close the whole__ night through?_____

$D^\flat$ $B^\flat m$ $E^{\flat 7}$

nice?

nice?

rit.   **Slower**

You know it seems the more we talk a - bout it,

ah

29

it on - ly makes it worse to live   with - out___ it,_____ but let's

ah   Live   with - out___ it,_____ but let's

A♭/C   Cm   B♭m⁷

a tempo

talk   a - bout___ it.   Oh, would-n't it___ be

talk   a - bout___ it.   Oh, would-n't it___ be

a tempo

Cm   B♭m⁷   E♭

Track Listing

1. Don't Worry Baby
(Wilson/Christian) Westminster Music Limited
Full Performance

2. God Only Knows
(Wilson/Asher) Universal Music Publishing Limited
Full Performance

3. Good Vibrations
(Wilson/Love) Universal Music Publishing Limited
Full Performance

4. In My Room
(Wilson/Usher) Universal Music Publishing Limited
Full Performance

5. Wouldn't It Be Nice
(Wilson/Asher/Love) Universal Music Publishing Limited
Full Performance

6. Don't Worry Baby
(Wilson/Christian) Westminster Music Limited
Piano Accompaniment

7. God Only Knows
(Wilson/Asher) Universal Music Publishing Limited
Piano Accompaniment

8. Good Vibrations
(Wilson/Love) Universal Music Publishing Limited
Piano Accompaniment

9. In My Room
(Wilson/Usher) Universal Music Publishing Limited
Piano Accompaniment

10. Wouldn't It Be Nice
(Wilson/Asher/Love) Universal Music Publishing Limited
Piano Accompaniment